Dipper
gets stuck

Written by Monica Hughes

Illustrated by Robert McPhillips

Dipper was a dolphin.
She was happy in the sea.
One day Dipper went to play
with some big dolphins.

The big dolphins swam
under the waves.
So did Dipper.

The big dolphins swam
over the waves.
So did Dipper.

Dipper jumped up out of the sea.
She saw a boat and
went over to it.

But then the boat went off.

Dipper went too.

'Stop! Stop!' said the big dolphins.

'Don't go, Dipper!'

The boat went on the sand.
Dipper went on the sand too.
'Help!' said Dipper.
'I don't like it here.'

The big dolphins saw Dipper.
'Get off the sand, Dipper,'
they said. 106

Dipper tried and tried but she
could not get off the sand.

A wave came up the sand.
'Get to the wave,'
said the big dolphins.
Dipper tried and tried but she
could not get to the wave.

Then a big wave came up the sand.
'Come on, Dipper,' said the dolphins.
'You can do it!
You can get to the wave.'

The big wave came up over Dipper.
Dipper jumped into the wave
and swam into the sea.

Dipper was very happy.
So were the big dolphins.
They swam off over the sea. 94